ODYSSEUS and the CYCLOPS and Other Plays

compiled by Irene Yates

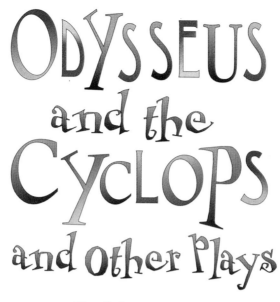

Contents

How to Read the Plays

The three plays in this book are for you to read aloud in small groups. There are six parts in each play, including the narrator in the first two plays. If your group is smaller than six, the narrator's part could be read by one of the characters.

Follow the play carefully and when it is your turn to speak, remember to say your part clearly. Try to speak the way your character would talk. If you think your character is loud and bossy then you should read the part in a loud bossy voice. If you are reading the part of a king or somebody very important, try to convey this in the way you read your lines.

1 Skim through the play and look over your parts.

2 Read your lines quietly to yourself.

3 Read the play aloud in your group.

4 Re-read the play and make sure that you use the right sort of voice for your character.

5 Swap roles and read the part of a different character.

Odysseus and the Cyclops

A Greek Myth
by Paul Copley

Illustrations by Keith Collman

Narrator

Odysseus

Polyphemus
(The Cyclops)

Nik

Alex

Andreas

Odysseus and the Cyclops

Scene 1 ***On board Odysseus' ship***

Narrator *The Trojan war had lasted ten hard years. At last it was over and the victorious Greeks set sail for home. But a violent storm scattered their great fleet of sailing ships. Odysseus had kept his twelve ships together but now they were in strange and unknown waters. They were running out of food and water.*

Odysseus *(In a strong firm voice)* Keep a sharp look-out, my friends. Shout if you spy land!

Narrator *Odysseus was a great hero – brave, wise and full of good ideas. On board were his closest friends – Nik, Alex and Andreas.*

Nik I am very worried, Odysseus. We have no food to eat nor water to drink, only a cask of strong wine in the hold.

Odysseus You are right, Nik. We must find land and take on fresh supplies.

Narrator *Odysseus and his men scanned the horizon looking for land. Then suddenly Alex gave a shout.*

Alex Look, Odysseus! There on the horizon. Land!

Narrator *Odysseus and his men headed for the distant horizon and cautiously approached the land.*

Andreas Look! Green grass. The island must have fresh water.

Nik I can see sheep and goats.

Alex At last! Meat to eat and milk to drink!

Andreas There's the shore. Let's land now!

Odysseus   Wait! We must be very careful. We don't know who lives on this island.

Nik   Well, I can't see anyone at all – not a single person.

Alex   And we're not scared of sheep and goats.

Andreas   No, we are fearless Greek warriors and we have just won a great victory.

Odysseus   So we have. But we must still be careful. Bring the cask of strong wine. If we meet somebody we may need it as a present.

Narrator   *Odysseus hid his ships behind some tall rocks. Taking just one ship, he landed on the island with twelve of his friends.*

Scene 2   **On the island**

Narrator   *When they reached the cliff top they found a deep, dark cave. Just outside, lambs and kids skipped and jumped in sheep pens.*

Nik   I wonder where the shepherd is?

Andreas   He'll be out tending the rest of his flock.

Alex   He must live in this cave.

Odysseus   We'll wait for him to come back. He must be a huge fellow. Just look at the size of those cheeses.

Nik   I've never seen such big jugs of milk.

Odysseus   Nik, Andreas, put our cask of strong wine at the back of the cave.

Andreas   Come on, Nik.

Alex   I'm starving. Can we eat some of this cheese, Odysseus?

Odysseus   Yes, and when the shepherd comes back, we'll pay for our supper.

Scene 3   *Inside the cave*

Narrator   *Night fell before they had finished eating. The cave was a very gloomy place. The only light was coming from the glowing embers of the fire in the middle of the floor. Nik and Andreas kept watch at the doorway. Suddenly the ground began to tremble and shake. They could hear boulders crunching and stones crashing down the cliffs into the sea below.*

Alex   *(In a terrified voice)* It's an earthquake!

Odysseus   It sounds more like the footsteps of a giant.

Nik   Look out, look out!

Andreas   There *is* a giant coming.

Nik   He's as big as twenty men.

Alex   That's big!

Andreas   He's so big that he's using a tree for a walking stick.

Alex   That's really big.

Nik   His face is hairy and dirty and as big as the moon.

Andreas   His teeth are like mouldy tree stumps.

Nik   And he's only got one eye.

Odysseus   Only one eye?

Nik   One massive round eye in the middle of his huge dirty forehead.

Narrator   *At that moment they all heard the great rumbling voice of Polyphemus the Cyclops. The ground shook as he spoke to his sheep and goats.*

Polyphemus   (In a booming voice) Here we are my beauties! Home at last! I'm ready for my supper now. I'm sure I could eat a dozen men and still not be full!

Nik   Hear that? What are we going to do, Odysseus?

Odysseus   Ssh! Quietly now. We must run and hide at the back of the cave. Quick!

Narrator   *As Odysseus and his friends watched from the shadows, the huge and terrible Cyclops milked all his goats and his sheep. Then he pulled a great lump of stone across the doorway of the cave. Odysseus whispered to his friends …*

Odysseus   (In a whisper) Now we are trapped. Even if we could get past the giant it would take more than twenty men to move that stone.

Polyphemus   What's that? Somebody's whispering? Somebody in my cave? Who's there?

Alex   He's heard us with those great hairy ears of his.

Nik   He's putting wood on the fire.

Andreas   The flames are lighting up the cave.

Alex   He'll see us!

Polyphemus   Aha! Now I see you! Stand still! People! Little people! Strange little people hiding in my cave. Who are you? What are you doing here? Speak!

Nik Be careful, Odysseus.

Odysseus Sir, we are Greeks trying to get home after ten years of war. Please be kind to us. As you know, the gods punish those who harm strangers!

Polyphemus Really? I don't think so, little stranger. You see, I am Polyphemus the Cyclops and I don't know what fear is. I'm not afraid of the gods. Tell me, where did you leave your ships?

Nik (*Quietly*) Oh no! He will sink all our ships!

Andreas   We will never get home.

Polyphemus   Speak up, I can't hear you!

Odysseus   Sir…we landed in only one ship.

Alex   *(Quietly)* Well done, Odysseus!

Odysseus   There are just thirteen of us here. We have just one ship to carry us back home.

Polyphemus   Home? You are not going home. You are not going anywhere. Come here! Come to me, I'm hungry! Come on!

Nik Oh no. He is going to eat us!

Odysseus *(Quietly)* Quickly, hide in the shadows.

Andreas Too late. He has caught two of our shipmates!

Polyphemus Mmmm! Supper! First you, in my left hand. Yum yum!

Alex He has eaten him. He's crunched him up, clothes, bones and everything!

Polyphemus Now you, in my right hand! Mmmm! Yum yum yum!

Nik Look at that. Swallowed him whole. He'll eat us all up!

Andreas Only eleven of us left.

Nik What shall we do, Odysseus? He'll eat us all if we don't escape.

Polyphemus Mmmm, very tasty, very sweet. Now, time for bed I think.

Narrator *Polyphemus settled down to sleep and the cave shook with his snores. Next morning he ate two more friends of Odysseus. Then he closed up the cave and left with his sheep.*

Nik He's gone.

Andreas Only nine of us left.

Alex   We are trapped.

Nik   There is nothing we can do.

Odysseus   Oh yes there is. Polyphemus has left his walking stick behind. Help me to drag it to the fire.

Narrator   *Odysseus drew his sword. He sharpened one end of the tree trunk until it looked like a great pointed pencil. Then they hardened the point in the fire and hid their new weapon under the dung heap.*

Odysseus   Just in time. The Cyclops is coming back. Nik and Andreas, bring me the cask of strong wine. I've got an idea.

Narrator *Suddenly Polyphemus was there inside the cave.*

Polyphemus Ah, there you are my tasty Greek heroes. Now, it's supper time! Who shall I eat first tonight?

Odysseus Sir, you must be very thirsty after your day's work. Please drink some of our wine.

Polyphemus Wine? You offer me wine?

Odysseus Yes, I do.

Nik Here it is!

Polyphemus Only one barrel! Still, I'll have a slurp. Mmmm, not bad. Not bad at all.

Odysseus Drink some more, please.

Polyphemus Yes, I will. Lovely. It's making me fizzy – I mean dizzy. What is your name?

Odysseus My name?

Polyphemus Yes. What's your name? I will drink to your health.

Nik *(Quietly)* He may let us go if you tell him who you are, Odysseus.

Odysseus *(Quietly)* This is a strange land, Nik. My name means nothing here. To him, I am nobody.

Polyphemus *(Loudly)* DON'T WHISPER!

Odysseus   You do not know me.

Polyphemus   That's right. So I want to know your name. WHAT IS IT?

Odysseus   I'm nobody. To you I am nobody.

Polyphemus   'NOBODY'? What an odd name. Well, Nobody – I'm feeling fizzy and dizzy and really quite fuzzy. Another sleep of this wine and I'm off to slurp! Er… I mean another slurp and I'm off to sleep!

Odysseus   You like the wine?

Polyphemus   I like the wine so much that I'm going to be kind to you, Nobody. I will still eat you, but I will be kind and eat you last of all! Ha – ha – haargh!

Narrator   *With an ugly laugh, the Cyclops leaned forward. He scooped up two more Greek warriors and swallowed them whole. He took another gulp of wine and fell to the floor of the cave in a drunken sleep. Odysseus ran to the dung heap and dragged out the sharpened wooden stake.*

Odysseus   *(Whispering to his men)* Quickly, take hold. We will use this as a spear.

Alex   He will wake up and eat us.

Odysseus   Not if he cannot see us.

Narrator   *Odysseus' men took a firm hold of the wooden stake. Then they ran at the snoring giant who had eaten six of their friends. They drove the point of their spear straight into the great bloodshot eye of Polyphemus, who let out a terrifying roar of pain and rage.*

Polyphemus   WAAAAAAARRRGGGGHHHHH!!!!

Narrator   *The cry was so loud that other Cyclopes in other caves heard it. They lumbered sleepily towards the cave shouting to Polyphemus – 'What's all the noise about? Is somebody in there with you? Is somebody trying to kill you?' Polyphemus shouted back to them…*

Polyphemus Nobody! Nobody is trying to kill me! Nobody is here in my cave!

Narrator *'Nobody? Then what is all the fuss about?' they grumbled. 'All that noise for nothing!' And off they went, back to their own caves.*

Odysseus Listen. The other Cyclopes have gone.

Nik They probably think Polyphemus has had a bad dream.

Andreas *(Quietly)* He can't see us, he'll never catch us now.

Alex But we are still trapped here in his cave.

Odysseus We will wait patiently, my friends. In the morning he will have to let his sheep out of the cave to graze. Then we will escape.

Scene 4 *The next morning at the cave*

Narrator *At first light the sheep started bleating. Polyphemus blundered to the cave entrance and opened it. Then his terrible voice rang round the cave.*

Polyphemus Listen to me, Nobody. Are you listening to me?

Andreas Nobody is listening to you.

Nik Ha ha! That's right. Nobody's listening!

Odysseus Ssh! Be careful, my friends.

Polyphemus Nobody – you think you are very clever but you will not escape. The only way you will leave this cave is inside my belly! Because I'm going to eat you all for breakfast!

Alex Look, he is sitting at the mouth of his cave.

Nik   He is checking all his sheep!

Andreas   Running his hands over them to make sure we are not hiding amongst them.

Odysseus   *(In a whisper)* Listen, my friends. I have another idea.

Narrator   *Using Polyphemus' own twine, Odysseus set to work. He tied the sheep together in groups of three. Then he bound each of his men underneath the middle sheep of each set of three. When the sheep ran out of the cave into the sunshine, blind Polyphemus ran his hands over their backs and sides. But he didn't find any of the Greek warriors. They quickly ran and hid behind the rocks.*

Scene 5 *Outside the cave*

Andreas We have escaped.

Nik We are all free.

Andreas No, we are not. Odysseus is still inside the cave.

Alex Look, here he comes. He is hiding underneath the biggest ram in the flock.

Andreas Polyphemus has stopped him.

Nik I can't bear to look!

Narrator *Odysseus was clinging to the thick curly wool underneath Polyphemus' favourite ram. Polyphemus stroked its noble head.*

Polyphemus Ah, my brave friend. That villain, Nobody, has robbed me of my sight. When I catch him, he will wish he'd never been born.

Andreas What is he saying?

Alex Has he caught Odysseus?

Nik Ssh! I can't hear.

Polyphemus You see, my fine woolly friend, I am going to eat Nobody up. But before I do, I will make him scream for mercy and beg for his life. Off you go now, my old friend, and lead your flock to the pasture.

Nik He has let the ram go.

Andreas It is trotting towards us.

Alex Odysseus has escaped. Look, here he comes.

Odysseus   Come my friends, follow me down the cliff path. Quickly.

Scene 6   ***On board Odysseus' ship***

Narrator   *Odysseus and his Greek warriors pushed off from the shore and pulled on the oars. As they sailed out to sea, Odysseus could see Polyphemus on the cliff top. He shouted up to the Cyclops…*

Odysseus   Cruel Cyclops, listen to me. You think that Nobody blinded you. But it was I who robbed you of your sight. And I am not Nobody. I am Odysseus the Greek warrior.

Narrator   *Polyphemus howled with rage!*

Polyphemus   WAAAARGH!! My curses on you, Odysseus. May you never reach home. If you do, may you never find happiness!

Odysseus   Your curses do not frighten me, Cruel One!

Narrator   *Polyphemus flung great rocks at Odysseus and his men. But the rocks missed their target and soon the ship was out of range.*

Nik   Can we go home now, Odysseus?

Odysseus   We certainly can. Pull on those oars my fine friends.

Nik   Hurray!

Alex   Hurray!

Andreas   Hurray!

Odysseus   Steer a course for Ithaca and home!

Narrator   *Away Odysseus sailed with his twelve ships across the silver sea. Another adventure lay in store over the horizon. But that's another story!*

How did Odysseus trick Polyphemus?

Find examples where Odysseus was 'brave, wise and full of good ideas'.

The Tailor of Thebes

A Traditional Tale
by Angela Lanyon
Illustrations by Rosalind Hudson

Narrator

The Shop Owner

Prince Omar

Labakan

The Pharaoh

The Queen

The Tailor of Thebes

Scene 1   *A tailor's shop in the bazaar*

Narrator   *This story happened in Egypt, in the city of Thebes, a very long time ago. Labakan, a tailor is sewing a caftan.*

Labakan   Stitch, stitch, stitch, that's all I ever do. I'm meant for a better life than this. I bet I'm really the son of the Pharaoh and got lost as a child.

(Enter the Shop Owner)

Shop Owner   Now then, Labakan, grumbling as usual. If you sewed as much as you grumbled you'd be the best tailor in Thebes.

Labakan I keep thinking of all the things I could have if I were rich.

Shop Owner Then start sewing and stop day-dreaming. Here's a robe belonging to a prince. Mend it quickly. There'll be extra money for you.

(The Shop Owner holds up the robe)

Labakan Why, that robe's just my size.

Shop Owner Forget about that and start sewing.

Narrator *The Shop Owner went away and Labakan picked up the robe.*

Labakan I'm sure this was made for me. Look at the style and the embroidery! I bet if I wear it everyone will think I'm a prince.

Narrator *Labakan tried the robe on and admired himself. He put his old caftan aside.*

Labakan Don't I look wonderful? I bet there's no one as handsome as me.

Narrator *The Shop Owner called from the shop.*

Shop Owner Labakan, I hope you're not wasting your time?

Labakan *(Calling)* Don't worry, master, my needle's red hot.

Narrator *But Labakan was not working. He left his needle and threads and started to climb out of the window.*

Labakan *(Muttering to himself)* Silly old goat. Why should I sew all day? Now that I'm dressed like this no one will know I'm a tailor. If I borrow it tonight everyone will think I'm a prince.

Narrator *Now as Labakan rode home on his old donkey a sandstorm blew up. When it was over, Labakan found himself far away from Thebes.*

Scene 2   A road in the desert

Labakan   This place looks strange. I wonder where I am? There's an oasis over there. Perhaps I'll find someone who can tell me where I am.

Narrator   *Just then a finely dressed young man rode up on a camel. He wore a richly embroidered robe and was going in the same direction as Labakan.*

Prince Omar   Greetings, friend. Where are you from?

Labakan   I'm from Thebes but I'm heading for the oasis.

Prince Omar   I am going there too. The road is long and if we ride together we'll be company for each other. But why is someone as well dressed as you only riding a donkey?

Labakan   *(Thinking quickly of an excuse)* Er…er, I'm fulfilling a vow – to the priests.

Prince Omar   And so am I. My name is Prince Omar and my father, the Pharaoh, sent me away when I was a child because my life was in danger. Now, after twenty years, I'm riding to meet him for the first time.

Labakan   If he's the Pharaoh, why aren't you going to the palace?

Prince Omar   I've got to go to the obelisk in the desert and he'll be there waiting for me.

Labakan   But how will he know who you are? He has not seen you for twenty years.

Narrator   *The Prince pulled a dagger out of his belt and showed it to Labakan. The hilt was studded with precious stones.*

Prince Omar You see this dagger? I've worn it ever since I was a child. I remember saying goodbye to my father in the Temple of Horus many miles up the river. When we meet I must say, 'The blessing of Horus be on you', and then he'll know I'm his son.

Labakan That all sounds wonderful, Prince Omar. I expect your father will be pleased to see you.

Prince Omar   Of course he will, and so will my mother. In a couple of days I shall be proclaimed my father's heir.

Narrator   *The two men rode on together and soon arrived at the oasis.*

Scene 3   ***An oasis in the desert***

Labakan   The oasis at last! I'm ready for a sleep, aren't you?

Narrator   *Prince Omar and Labakan tied their animals to a palm tree.*

Prince Omar   Sleep well, my friend. In two days' time I shall see my father.

Narrator   *They wrapped themselves in blankets and the prince fell asleep. Labakan sat and looked at him.*

Labakan I don't know why he's a prince and I'm just a tailor. My robe is as good as his and I'm sure I'd make just as good a prince. If I take his dagger and his camel and get to the obelisk before him, maybe the Pharaoh will make me his heir. After all, if he hasn't seen Prince Omar for twenty years he won't know the difference.

Narrator *Very carefully, Labakan crept up to the prince, eased the dagger from his belt and slipped it into his own. Then he went to the palm trees and untied the Prince's camel.*

Labakan *(Laughing to himself)* Farewell, Labakan the tailor, I am Prince Omar now.

35

Scene 4   The Pharaoh's camp

Narrator   *Two days later, deep in the desert by the obelisk, the Pharaoh and the Queen waited for their son, the Prince, to arrive. They were both excited.*

Queen   Lord Pharaoh, I've had so many dreams about my son, I can't wait to see him.

Pharaoh   *(Pointing)* Look over there at that cloud of sand. That must be him.

Queen   It is, it is! And soon I shall see his face!

Narrator   *Everyone cheered as Labakan rode up to the obelisk. He got off his camel and presented the jewel-studded dagger to the Pharaoh.*

Labakan   The blessing of Horus be on you.

Pharaoh   This is indeed my son. Welcome, Prince Omar.

Labakan   Ever since we parted at the Temple of Horus I have looked forward to today.

Queen   *(Surprised)* But this isn't my son.

Pharaoh   What do you mean?

Queen   He doesn't look like the son I've seen in my dreams.

Pharaoh   What good are dreams, my Queen, when the Prince is here?

Narrator   *There was more shouting as the real Prince Omar rode up on Labakan's donkey.*

Prince Omar   *(Angrily)* I am Prince Omar! This man has taken my place.

Pharaoh   But he has the dagger.

Prince Omar   He stole it from me.

Labakan   *(Indignant)* This fellow is lying. He followed me all the way from Thebes. He is nothing but a half-crazed tailor who has stolen a rich man's robes.

Prince Omar   He speaks of himself. *He* is the thief. He stole my dagger and my camel.

Narrator   *The Pharaoh beckoned his guards and pointed to Prince Omar.*

Pharaoh   Guards, seize this crazy man and tie him up.

Queen   Oh Pharaoh, I'm sure I'd recognise my son, but this man who calls himself Prince Omar…

Pharaoh   He is my son. Let it be proclaimed.

Scene 5   *Later that night in the Pharaoh's tent*

Queen   Lord Pharaoh, I know you are all wise but I'm still worried about Prince Omar. Will you promise me something?

Pharaoh   Anything you ask.

Queen   I would so like a new robe for when he's proclaimed Prince. Couldn't he make one for me?

Pharaoh   My son, make a robe?

Queen   You promised, and I'm sure the crazy one couldn't do anything like that.

Pharaoh   All right, all right. In the morning we shall give them both needles and threads but you must promise to wear whatever he makes.

Queen   I promise!

Scene 6   *Three days later in the throne room of the palace*

Narrator   *Labakan entered the throne room and held up the caftan he had made for the Queen.*

Labakan   Here you are, my mother, the finest caftan that has ever been seen. Look at the tiny stitching and the neat hems.

Narrator   *Then Prince Omar came in. He threw down the material and the needle and thread.*

Prince Omar   There's your caftan, O Queen. I've learnt to ride and shoot and hunt. I've learnt to throw spears and kill enemies, but the stitching of caftans is not work for a prince.

Narrator   *Labakan looked frightened and realised the queen had tricked them.*

Queen Lord Pharaoh, when we parted from our son, didn't the High Priest give you two boxes telling us to offer them to the Prince so he might choose his future?

Pharaoh He did.

Queen And can he choose now?

Narrator *Pharaoh clapped his hands and a servant entered with two small boxes.*

Queen These boxes have never been opened since the High Priest gave them to us.

Pharaoh *(To Labakan)* Choose, my son. Lay your hand on the box that contains your future.

Labakan Let me see. Two boxes – both covered with precious stones. This one has 'wealth and happiness' written on it. I can see no greater happiness than being the Pharaoh's son and no greater wealth than I shall have as his heir. I will choose this one.

Pharaoh Now sit beside the Queen.

Narrator *Then Pharaoh pointed to Prince Omar.*

Pharaoh Now you, you crazy tailor from Thebes – make your choice.

Narrator *Prince Omar spent a long time looking at the boxes.*

Prince Omar   'Honour and glory' is written on this other box. In the last two days the happiness I expected has been destroyed and the riches I had have been stolen. I'll choose 'honour and glory'. The honour of being truthful and the glory of doing what is right.

Pharaoh   Now you have both chosen – open the boxes and let me see.

Narrator   *Labakan opened his box first. His mouth dropped open.*

Labakan   A needle and thread!

Narrator   *Then Prince Omar opened the other box.*

Prince Omar   The red and white crown of Egypt!

Pharaoh   Then you must be my son.

Queen   *(The Queen points to Labakan)* So you *are* the crazy tailor of Thebes!

Narrator   *Labakan fell on his knees in fear.*

Labakan   Forgive me, Lord Pharaoh. I am only a stupid tailor with ambitions too big for my workshop.

Pharaoh   I'm so happy at having my son back that I'll forgive you, but get on your donkey and go back to Thebes before I change my mind.

Labakan   Can you forgive me, Prince Omar?

Prince Omar   Go in peace. But next time, beware. You may not get off so lightly.

Pharaoh   Well done, my son – spoken like a true prince.

Narrator   *Labakan rushed out of the throne room, took his donkey and rode back to Thebes as quickly as he could.*

Scene 7   **The tailor's shop in Thebes some days later**

Narrator   *Labakan ran to the tailor's shop. The Shop Owner was standing by the door.*

Labakan   Master, master, please forgive me for running away.

Shop Owner   You are a thief and rogue, Labakan! You deserve to be punished.

Labakan   But here is the robe. I'm wearing it.

Narrator   *The Shop Owner went red in the face. He was angry.*

Shop Owner   And look at the state it's in – torn round the hem and covered with sand. Take it off and get out. I'm not going to give you a job any longer.

Labakan   But if I haven't any work I shall starve.

Narrator *The Shop Owner pointed to Labakan's box.*

Shop Owner What's that you're holding? You could sell that box. It's probably worth something.

Labakan What a good idea, then I can buy some cloth and start my own business.

Shop Owner What? You run a shop? And I suppose you think you'll be the best tailor in Thebes.

Narrator *Labakan took off the tattered robe, put on his old caftan and slunk out of the shop.*

Narrator *Labakan sold the box but he kept the needle and thread that were in the box. With the money, he was able to buy some fine cloth. So the next day Labakan sat down and started to sew.*

Scene 8 **Inside Labakan's house**

Labakan How very strange, this needle seems to sew all by itself and the stitches are the neatest I have ever seen. And however much thread I use, it never runs out.

Narrator *Labakan worked hard every day sewing with the needle and thread that the Pharaoh had given him. People from all over Thebes came to buy his fine clothing and he was soon able to buy a workshop.*

Labakan These gifts from the High Priest are greatly to be treasured. I made a good choice when I chose 'wealth and happiness'. My clothes sell for high prices and I am certainly happy.

Narrator *As the years went by, Labakan became known not only as the best tailor in Thebes but the best tailor in the whole of Egypt. Never again did he want to wear robes that didn't belong to him or pretend to be someone he wasn't.*

How did the Queen determine who was her son?

How did a needle and thread bring Labakan 'wealth and happiness'?

London's Burning

A Performance Poem
by Irene Yates

Illustrations by Lucy Bristow

Voice 1

Voice 2

Voice 3

Voice 4

Voice 5

Voice 6

London's Burning

Voice 1   It is Sunday, the second of September.

Voice 2   It's one of those days
In the hot, dry summer
Of sixteen sixty six.

Voice 3   There's been no rain
For weeks and weeks.

Voice 4   Everything is parched and dry.
The grass is shrivelled,
The earth scorched.

Voice 5   If only it would rain.

Voice 6   The city of London sleeps,
As much as it can ever sleep.
For London is busy day and night.

Voice 1   The streets are narrow,
And dirty.

Voice 2   No bigger than alleyways.

Voice 3   The houses have timber frames
And the walls are made of mud –
Plastered on to woven sticks.

Voice 4   People call this wattle and daub.

Voice 5   The houses have three storeys,
Each overhanging the one below.

Voice 6   In some places the tops of the buildings
Meet across the narrow streets.

Voice 1   Wealthy merchants buy and sell,
Tradesmen call their wares.

Voice 2   Ships leave the docks,
Travel the world,
Bring back spices, silks
And all kinds of riches.

Voice 3   In Pudding Lane, the bakery
Is closed.

Voice 4   The baker and his whole household
Are in bed
Above the shop.

Voice 5   Then disaster strikes.

Voice 6   At two o'clock in the morning
The dry wood in the baker's kitchen –
No one knows quite how –
Ignites.

Voice 1   First, a tiny spark –
And then a glow –
And then the whole pile
Bursts into flames.

All voices   *(Whisper slowly and steadily)*
I am the fire, I am the fire,
Glowing, crackling, spitting, flickering –
I am the fire, I am the fire,
Looking for somewhere to go,
Tumbling and spreading,
Certain to grow.

Voice 2 A servant stirs in his sleep.
The smell of smoke fills his nostrils.
He goes down to the bakery and
Finds the fire.

With fingers of fear
Clutching at his heart
He wakes the household.

Voice 3 By the time everyone is up
The entire bakery is ablaze.

Voice 4 The flames of the fire dance upwards.

Voice 5 All in the household rush towards the roof,
Screaming for help.
They leap on to their neighbour's building
And wake them with their cries.

Voice 6 The angry flames follow.

Voice 1 The neighbours leap on to the roof next
door,
And their neighbours on to the next,
And so it goes on –
Until the whole of Pudding Lane
Is awake and
Desperate to escape the fire.

Voice 2 But the angry flames follow.

Voice 3 Scarlet flames flare round every house
and shop.
The sky glows crimson
And sparks whirl upwards like a zillion
silver stars.

All voices *(Louder and a little bit faster)*
I am the fire, I am the fire,
Glowing, crackling, spitting, flickering –
I am the fire, I am the fire,
Scrambling and scurrying,
Roaring and tumbling,
Hurrying, hurrying, hurrying…

Voice 4   People run –
Screaming with fright –
Fleeing from their burning houses.

Voice 5   They pile their belongings into sacks –
Haul their furniture on to carts –
Pack everything they can save
Into pockets and skirts
And hasten to leave the flames behind.

Voice 6   In the streets, the horses bolt,
Terrified by the fire.

Voice 1   Houses collapse with a terrible crash.

Voice 2   The air roars as the fire
Travels from building to building,
Whipped into frenzy
By a fierce east wind.

Voice 3   The people rush, as a crowd, to the river.

Voice 4   Ferrymen put out their hands
To haul the people into their boats.

Voice 5   Gratefully they fling handfuls of coins
At the ferrymen's feet.

Voice 6   The boats huddle under the bridges for
safety
And the people gaze in fear
As the flames spread.

Voice 1   Troops of fire-fighters march toward the fire
With leather buckets full of water
They've filled from the taps in the street
That bring piped water from the river.

The people work desperately at the pumps,
But there's been a drought
And the river is low
So there's hardly any water in the pipes.

Voice 2   It is hopeless.

Voice 3   And the fire grows.

Voice 4   It rages down to the warehouse –
Along the riverside –
And licks its way
Around the wooden buildings
Causing such suffocating fumes
That people choke as they
Run through the streets.

All voices   *(Loud, fast and furious)*
I am the fire! I am the fire!
Roaring! Hissing! Sizzling! Leaping!
I am the fire! I am the fire!
Quick and curious,
Fierce and furious,
I destroy all in my path.
I am the fire!
Yes, I am the fire!

Voice 5 Above the city of London, a huge black cloud
Of soot and smoke
Blots out the sky.

Voice 6 The King issues orders. He announces –

Voice 1 Make special fire posts throughout the city –
Send them equipment and food and drink.
The people must work together,
The soldiers will have to help.
We HAVE TO save the city from this fire!

Voice 2 Still, the fire grows.

Voice 3 It eats up St Paul's Cathedral,

Voice 4 The Royal Exchange,

Voice 5 The Guildhall, where the Mayor sits.

Voice 6   And Bridewell,
Where the city's store of grain is kept.

Voice 1   Can nothing stop this fire in its tracks?

Voice 2   The Duke of York has a plan. He wonders –

Voice 3   Suppose the fire had nowhere else to go,
Nothing else to burn –
Perhaps it would die out.

Voice 4   The Duke is right!
We must make a fire-break –
A gap that the angry flames cannot cross.
If we pulled down all the buildings
That stand in the path of the fire –

Voice 5   Before they catch alight –

Voice 6   The fire would surely die!

Voice 1   A fire-break will save the city.

Voice 2   Pull down the wooden wharves at the Fleet river!

Voice 3   Pull down the wooden houses each side!

Voice 4   Pull down anything that's in the path of the fire!

Voice 5   Make a clear way!

Voice 6   Thud! Thud! Thud!
Goes the gunpowder
In the distance –
Blowing up buildings
To make the fire-break.

All voices   *(Slow and hesitating)*
I am the fire, I am the fire.
Smouldering, smoking, turning to ash.
I am the fire, I am the fire,
Faltering, sighing,
My flames dying.
I am the fire,
I am the…
I am…

Voice 1   By Wednesday, the fifth of September,
The strong wind has dropped.

Voice 2   The fire is brought under control.

Voice 3   The fire-break has worked –
It has held the flames back.

Voice 4   But the city lies in ruins,
Almost all of it burned to the ground.

Voice 5   Thirteen thousand homes and
Hundreds of important buildings gone forever.

Voice 6   Families camp in tents and burned-out shelters –
Anything for a roof.

Voice 1   Devastation –

Voice 2   Heartbreak –

Voice 3   The whole city destroyed
From one small spark.

Voice 4   The King speaks.

Voice 5   We will rebuild the city.
It will be rebuilt swiftly and safely.
It will be planned and designed so that
Fire will never sweep its streets again.
Our new London will be great!

All voices   *(Beginning softly, becoming louder)*
We are the city, We are the city,
See London now
Risen from the ashes.
All our buildings brick and stone –
All our streets wide and straight –
All our bridges free from clutter –
We are the city, We are the city,
Risen and rebuilt.
We are the city –
Busy –
Prosperous –
Important –

Voice 6   We are the city, We are the city,

Voices 3, 4   We are the city, We are the city,

Voices 1, 2, 5, 6   We are the city –

All voices   We are the city,
More magnificent than ever!

How does this play differ from the other plays?

Why do you think the author chose to write it in this way?